God's Diary

God's Diary

Some excerpts selected by

H. J. RICHARDS

Twenty-Third Publications, Mystic, Connecticut • The Columba Press, Dublin

1991

First edition 1991
published, in the United States of America, by
Twenty-Third Publications
185 Willow Street
P.O. Box 180
Mystic, CT 06355
(203)536-2611

ISBN 0-89622-474-0
Library of Congress Catalog Card Number 90-71819

and, in Ireland, by
The Columba Press
93, The Rise, Mount Merrion,
Blackrock, Co Dublin

ISBN 1-8560-026-3

Designed and illustrated by Bill Bolger

What a week this has been!
My sense of eternal loneliness
grew so intense last Saturday
that I had an irresistible urge to be creative.
Overnight I planned six days of wild activity.
I would create a universe!
Land and sea, earth and sky, light and dark,
and a million constellations!
Thousands of varieties of growing things,
and even more of moving things!
Large and small, from insects to dinosaurs!

Yesterday, Friday, was the most exhausting.
How to populate this beautiful earth,
now that I had struggled so hard to rescue it
from the all-englobing seas?
I finally simply gave my imagination full rein,
and ran through the alphabet:

> apes and antelopes
> beavers and beetles
> cats and camels
> dodos and dinosaurs
> elephants and ewe-lambs
> giraffes and guernseys
> horses and hippopotamuses
> jackals and jerboas
> koalas and kangaroos
> moles and maggots
> pigs and panthers
> rabbits and rattlesnakes
> squirrels and spiders
> weevils and wombats
> zoophytes and zebras.

In my best Latin I issued the command *fiat*,
and they were there – or at least would be
when my laws of evolution took effect.

A brilliant afterthought came to me in the afternoon.
What about putting all this extravagant week's work
in charge of a creature in my own image and likeness?
Or why not two of them together, man and wife?
I gasped at the boldness of my plan.
This could be my masterpiece, my grand finale.

Pity perhaps that my first hasty efforts
produced humans
not all that different from this morning's chimpanzees.
On the other hand,
in a few hundred thousand years' time
they'll evolve into something more civilised.
And after all, we've got all the time in the world.

But I felt whacked when it was all over, and had to rest
all day today.

Shamayim! What a week it has been!

---

* *The Irish Archbishop Ussher will later tell me to start on this page.*
I've forgotten the actual date myself.

That afterthought of making Adam and Eve
'in my own image and likeness', brilliant as it was,
is beginning to cause problems.
How much like me do I really want them to be?
I've trustingly handed over control of my world
to them,
and conferred on them my own powers of creativity.
They are my colleagues, co-creators together with me.
But in calling them, metaphorically,
my son and daughter,
am I hoping they'll be for ever tied to my apron strings?
To be like me, won't they need to assert
their freedom and independence?

Today was a case in point.
Months ago I had installed them
in a glorious Garden City, a veritable paradise.
To establish my own absolute authority,
I had put an embargo on one of the fruit trees.
There was nothing special about the tree:
I was using it simply as a test case.
This afternoon I was horrified to discover that
first Eve, then Adam,
have deliberately been eating the fruit.
There were peelings all round the tree.
When I challenged them,
I was more horrified still by their reply:
If I didn't ultimately want them
to stand on their own feet and make their own decisions,
why did I make them in my image in the first place?

Had I been too successful?

I haven't solved this problem yet.

Perhaps I made a mistake
in forbidding them to eat the fruit.
Should I perhaps have forbidden them
to eat the serpent?

Nonetheless, to assert my sovereignty,
I had to evict them from the Garden.
They were both rather embarrassed
about being naked,
so I sewed them up two pairs of bikinis.
But Eve's contrite face moved me to tears.

Over these dull years,
I haven't been keeping my diary,
so little has happened.
But today my worst fears were confirmed:
this was obviously going to happen sooner or later.

Adam and Eve,
having introduced the problem of evil into the world
(or was it me?
After all, that wretched serpent was my handiwork!),
their two sons have compounded the matter
by attacking each other.
Which of them was at fault?
People will say, 'God knows,'
but I am as much in the dark as anyone else.
Whichever,
Cain has today turned on his brother Abel,
and killed him.

So these creatures of mine
have invented not only envy of me,
but envy of each other.
Not only pride, rebellion, jealousy and disobedience,
but now murder as well.
Where will it all end?

Oh, my poor creation!

It's going from bad to worse.
Last month I actually found myself
regretting I'd ever created anything in the first place.
Evil has become so endemic in my world,
it seemed the only sensible thing to do
was to wipe out all living creatures
and begin all over again.
My world needs a thorough wash.

So I decided to remove my heavenly dome,
and let the primeval waters engulf the earth again.
The relentless rain that ensued
has been like forty days of tears.

At the last minute I relented.
I've always been inconsistent.
I couldn't bring myself to drown Noah:
after all
he's eventually going to be the inventor of wine.
So I forewarned him about the flood,
and he built a houseboat as an asylum for his family
and a collection of animals.

Today they disembarked.
Their joy on re-entering a spring-cleaned earth
was so moving that I promised them – and myself –
that, however bad things got,
I'd never again do anything so drastic.
The human race is worth more
than the sum of all its sins.
I told Noah
to see the rainbow that came up this evening
as a reminder of this promise.

In spite of the fresh start I made with Noah,
we've come full circle back to Adam's sin again.
This week, the BCC
(Babylonian Construction Company)
has been putting the finishing touches
to its grandiose new cathedral – a stepped skyscraper
that, quite literally,
seems to be trying to dig a hole into heaven.
My divine privilege under threat again?
I scotched this blasphemous scheme very quickly.

There's a worrying ambiguity
about all temples and cathedrals.
I know they're meant to be a compliment to me.
But how they blinker people's understanding of me!

Perhaps it's time for another fresh start.
I have my eyes on a wandering Aramaean.
He looks very promising.

I made the right choice: I'm with Abraham all the way.
He's a rock you can build on.
I can see the whole future
looking back to this man in admiration.
His unconditional trust in me
is the first bit of really good news
since I launched this wild experiment.
His relationship with me
is the kind I've always been hoping for.

Which doesn't prevent him trying to haggle with me,
the other day, market fashion.
I played along with the game,
I like the fellow so much.

Nor does it prevent him
sharing some of the primitive views of his neighbours.
Today he even had the crazy notion that I'd be pleased
if he slit the throat of his only son Isaac in my honour!
I sent an angel quick to stop him.
Fortunately there was a lamb available,
so he sacrificed that instead.
I thought, 'Poor lamb',
but at least it was better than 'Poor Isaac'.

The name Isaac means Joy.
That's exactly what he is, both to me and to his parents.
He'll obviously inherit.
I only hope his Israelite descendants
won't start taking it out on their Arab neighbours.
Through Abraham's son Ishmael,
they are their blood brothers.

* The dates from here on, I'll be assured by scholars, are more reliable than poor old Ussher's. My apologies.

Abraham's family has grown into a sizeable clan,
now named after its current patriarch, Israel.
He's wisely changed his name from Jacob,
worried about the way people keep reminding him
that it means *Cheat* – which is what he is.

I'd hoped the clan would settle permanently
in Palestine – a piece of the world I'm very partial to.
But a famine forced many of them
to emigrate to Egypt,
and they've so warmed to its more luxurious life-style
that they look like settling there.
If they're ever going to uproot themselves
and go back to the land of their fathers and mothers,
it'll need a bombshell.

I've found my bombshell.
An Israelite youngster called Moses.
A bright lad, good grades at school,
and an Egyptian University degree
in Liberation Theology.
With most of the Israelites now press-ganged
into Pharaoh's new Brick Production Plant,
he's making the rounds
to arouse a Trades Union protest.
He's getting considerable support.

Moses has finally taken the plunge.
Infuriated by the cruelty
of an over-zealous Egyptian foreman,
he throttled him,
and then ran for his life into the desert.
There, repentant and reflective,
wondering what sort of a God
would so violently insist
that action must be taken to liberate the exploited,
he hit upon a Hebrew name for such a God:
'Yahweh' – 'God is what God is'.

He'd taken off his shoes
and was resting by a desert bush,
incandescent in the last rays of the evening sun.
I could only approve of his reverent refusal
to name the mystery that I am.

Things have moved fast.
Moses has returned to Egypt,
determined to stir things up.
He's rallied the Israelite families,
and called for a general walk-out.
He's receiving quite a bit of support,
though there are a few blacklegs:
in spite of the hard labour,
they find the Egyptian fleshpots
considerably more attractive than a long desert trek.

There's been a rather tedious competition
with the Egyptian court magicians,
who were naturally able to do tricks
quite as remarkable as the ones Moses
and his brother Aaron had prepared.
But Moses finally held the trump card.
Seizing on the idea of Israel being my 'first-born',
he's made it the main theme
of this year's spring sacrifice of lambs.

Nice thought,
and, in the light of my special relationship
with Abraham, Isaac and Jacob,
a justifiable claim.
But then Pharaoh and the Egyptians
are my children too.

Ought I to condone
the exclusive claims the Israelites are making?
Ought I to be taking sides at all?

A shrewd man, Moses.
A sudden freak epidemic among the Egyptians,
and he seized the opportunity.
'The hand of God', he megaphoned round the camps,
and the Israelites were off.

They were in luck.
The local Egyptian police
were today detailed to investigate
their illegal withdrawal of labour,
and, if necessary, force them to come back.
But the Egyptian transport
got bogged down in a swamp,
and the lumbering Israelite caravan
is heading for the desert.

I notice the Egyptians
are not writing this event up in their chronicles.
Fair enough.
After all,
the labour force only consists of a few thousand.
But I'm writing it up enthusiastically in my chronicle.

Moses has finally brought the Israelite clans
to the foot of mount Sinai.
He has a great affection for this place.
He feels close to me here,
and spends days at a time alone on the mountain.
When he comes down to speak to his people,
his face is glowing with light,
as though he'd been speaking to me, face to face.

In these days of meditation and silence,
he has painfully simplified,
into ten basic sentences,
the rules by which people ought to live,
and chiselled them out on two stone tablets.
Today he presented them to Israel.
They solemnly accepted them,
and swore to live by them.
My blessings on this people.
They have a lot to teach the world.

I was thinking that the Israelites
have a lot to teach the world.
But they've also a lot to learn.
Last week, at Sinai,
after a series of complaints
about Moses's interminable invisible communings
with me,
they decided to make me visible
in the shape of a powerful bull.
A compliment in a way, I suppose.
But Moses was so angered
by this blatant transgression of his first commandment,
that he hoisted the two tablets of the Law
above his head,
and hurled them down on the rocks,
where they shattered into pieces.
Wearily, he took up the chisel again.

The bull had been Aaron's idea.
Moses tore strips off him,
and, for the rest of the day,
went around muttering about the disasters
that befall a world
where priests take precedence over prophets.

Then this week,
as the Israelites finally struck camp
to continue their journey,
there were further grumblings.
I've been providing them, over these months,
with an instant pre-sweetened breakfast cereal.
Very acceptable, I would have thought,

in a peninsula that provides precious little else to eat.
Ecstatically welcomed at first as 'bread from heaven',
it is now being greeted with,
'Oh no, not that b... manna again!'

This time it was I who got livid.
I even considered
getting shot of the whole idea of a chosen race.
I had a word about the matter with Moses.

He saw my point, but talked me round.

Moses has died, aged 120.
To the very end he never needed false teeth or glasses.
The Israelites wept for days.
So did I.

Of all my spokesmen – Adam, Noah, Abraham –
none has been so privy to my thoughts as Moses,
and all Israel spontaneously knew this to be so.
They'll never again be able to see me
except through the eyes of Moses.
And they'll henceforth always long for another
to complete the work he's begun.

What Moses has accomplished
will stand forever as an archetype.
The exodus from Egypt had its shortcomings:
there was far more hassle *en route*
than I would have liked.
But for all that,
people will always need to look back on this event
as a blueprint of my hopes for the human race.

When people are oppressed and exploited,
alienated and in exile,
I stand in exile alongside them.
Anyone who works to liberate them
from such ungodly situations
is my son,
in whom I am well pleased.

1209 BC Joshua
1207 BC Jericho
1205 BC Gibeon
1178 BC Ehud
1125 BC Deborah
1120 BC Gideon and Abimelech
1117 BC Jephthah
1102 - 1071 BC Some minor Judges,
whose names will be forever remembered by someone,
I hope.
1060 Samson.

These two centuries have been so busy,
wild and hilarious,
that I could do no more than jot down
a few names and dates.
For the record, now that things are more peaceful,
I should open out a few of the highlights.

Joshua turned out a worthy successor to Moses.
He finally brought the liberated slaves successfully
into their ancestral land,
to rejoin the relatives
who had not originally emigrated with them.
Palestine is not a rich country,
but compared with the desert
you could say it flows with milk and honey.

A lot of fighting, inevitably,
with the local inhabitants, who, naturally,
resented this wave of immigrant refugees.
At Jericho, for example,

where a broad-minded barmaid
helped things to a swift conclusion.
And at Gibeon,
where the Israelite victory was so overwhelming
that even the sun and moon stood agape.

But the land is large enough
to hold both Israelites and Canaanites,
and there really was no need
for the amount of slaughter that took place.
Some of the Israelites
seemed to think it
a sacred duty
to wipe out everyone in sight.
They even formed groups calling themselves
CAIN (Canaanites Awful, Israelites Nice)
and ETHEL (Exterminate The Lot).
They didn't succeed, I'm glad to say.

This, of course, caused difficulties
over the next 150 years,
with renewed squabbles about who runs this country.
In fact, under the leadership of great men and women,
the dispersed Israelites did recover
some kind of unity from time to time.
But it was touch and go.

Samson was something else.
He set up a sort of One-Man-Resistance-Movement,
and his escapades with the Philistines
gave us all a big laugh.
Being the clown he was,

it had to be him that finally brought the house down.

In this Israelite saga,
it's interesting that it was a non-Israelite
who showed the kind of loyalty
that really needs a book to be written
about mother-in-laws.
Ruth's devotion to Naomi
puts Israelite chauvinism to shame.
A king would be proud to point back
to such a woman as his ancestor.

A touching nativity story twelve years ago –
little Samuel unexpectedly born to ageing parents.
Anna's *Magnificat* was a superb recognition
of my preferential option for the poor.

A touching sequel recently –
the lad's been having nightmares and hearing voices.
He feels called to become a leader,
and senses that disaster is in store for Israel

He wasn't wrong.
Today the Israelites
took their clumsy sacrament of my presence
(imagine, a wooden box!)
into battle.
The Philistines now have it.

One can only wish them piles of luck!

With Eli dead (what a liability he was!),
Samuel has assumed the leadership of Israel
in its struggle against the Philistines.
A valiant and charismatic leader,
but I've never really warmed to him.
There's a devious and cruel streak in him.
He was right
to resist the movement to appoint an Israelite king –
I had always thought that I was king enough for them.
And he was also right
eventually to compromise with the popular demand,
stipulating that the king
could only be a stand-in for me.
But having anointed Saul,
how can he already be scheming for a replacement?
Treasonable, I would have thought.

Worse still,
having established kingship as something sacred,
how could he have butchered king Agag
in such a sickening way?
As if that's what I mean by obedience!

It is flattering some people to endure them.
But that's me.

I feel so sad about Saul.
He showed such promise,
head and shoulders above the rest.
He won the acclaim of all Israel,
and defended them brilliantly
against their enemies on all fronts.
The affection aroused by his son Jonathan,
his spitting image,
is a measure of the man's attractiveness.
It's only in this last year,
worn down by the antagonism of Samuel
claiming to speak in my name,
that he's become moody, depressive, even paranoid.

He died today.
Suicide.
Welcome home, my bruised son!

The accession of David
has been like the light at the end of the tunnel.
A dead shot with the sling, a dab hand on the guitar,
a dark brown voice, fifty gospel songs of his own
– what a godsend to cheer us all up again!

The Israelites took to him immediately,
first his own southerners,
then, a bit later, the northerners.
And when he captured Jerusalem earlier this year
(what a brainwave
to send commandos up the watershaft!)
he was the darling of all the tribes.
It was a masterstroke
to overcome the traditional animosity
between north and south
by focusing the attention of both of them
on to the almost forgotten Exodus and Moses.
He has rescued the Holy Box,
abandoned in some remote village,
and solemnly installed it in Jerusalem.
I acclaim him, as I did Saul,
as my son, my representative, my stand-in.

He has his shortcomings of course,
some shorter than others.
That devious period when he joined the Philistines
while he bided his time.
The protection racket he ran
to fund himself and his heavies.
The two occasions when he didn't hesitate
to commit murder (heavily disguised of course)

to add more attractive wives to his harem.
His insensitive relationship
with this numerous children
– guaranteed to lead to disaster.
In many ways he is a careerist
– shrewd, crafty, ruthless.

Yet when you get through to him,
he's basically an honest man,
with a humility that melts you.
When Nathan uncovered the Bathsheba affair,
David could have had him silenced, even 'taken out'.
Instead he broke down and asked for forgiveness.
Who could have refused him?

The songs he writes are jewels.
I like best those in praise of me,
the *tehillim* as he calls them in Hebrew.
The ones that expect me
to provide a whole host of things
– health, wealth, success, children, defeat of enemies,
reversal of bad luck, preservation from death,
you name it – I am not so sure about.
What do people honestly expect me
to be able to do for them?
Don't they realise how tied my hands are?
I must some time give more thought
to the strange phenomenon of petitionary prayer.
It worries me.

Meanwhile, David has brought the Exodus event
to a brilliant culmination.

To 'instal' me in Jerusalem,
symbolic though the action is,
is a perfect sequel to the work that Moses did.
People will always need to follow Moses
through a desert to achieve their freedom.
But they'll also need to enjoy that freedom
in my presence, in a Jerusalem built by David.

In spite of my praise of David,
his *mafioso* deathbed instructions
betray once again the shortcomings I noted earlier.
Unwilling to do his own dirty work
on the enemies he collected in his lifetime,
he's left Solomon to do it for him.

Poor Solomon!
Yet I feel in my bones
that this lad is going to bring about
a Golden Age surpassing even David's.

I wasn't wrong about Solomon.
We've had nearly thirty-two years of peace
with the neighbouring countries,
something that neither Saul nor David
ever managed to achieve
(what a shrewd move
to marry all those foreign princesses!)
He's transformed Jerusalem
from a village to an international capital,
and established it as a commercial centre
for the whole of the Middle East.
He's trained a whole army of scribes
to keep the growing records
of this newly fledged empire.
He's even started to make a collection of proverbs,
some of them his own originals.

I still have reservations about the imposing Temple
he's built for me alongside his palace
(he likes to feel he's sitting at my right hand).
I mean, I feel cramped enough in the vast heavens
where people locate me;
how on earth can this building contain me?
Isn't it bound, eventually,
to narrow people's understanding of me,
rather than expand it?
Yet it is breathtakingly beautiful,
and if it can instil into the people a sense of awe,
and of my closeness to them,
I'm happy to accept it, *pro tem*.

Solomon is dead.
How well he consolidated the achievements of David.
Because of him, the kingship experiment
is obviously going to thrive for a while yet.

Not that he was ever a mere caretaker of the past.
He forged boldly ahead,
and pioneered a whole host of new projects.
I was particularly interested in his open attitude
towards the religious practices
of the nations he married into.
He saw these nations as I do,
as being as genuinely my children as the Israelites are.
I doubt whether his people are yet mature enough
(or secure enough)
to take on board such ecumenical views.
It could take a thousand years.
Even two.
Perhaps three.

And in the light of such ingrained conservatism,
I'm afraid he'll get a bad press
in the official Israelite chronicles.
But in my book he's a paragon of wisdom.

Can there ever be a greater than Solomon?

Yes, I was right
about the Israelite slowness to follow Solomon's lead.
The conservative northerners,
only precariously at one with the southerners
at the best of times,
have gone off to form their own kingdom.
Highly confusing to future students,
who will now have two interminable lists of kings
to memorise.
But I've accepted the inevitable,
and am watching with interest to see what will ensue.

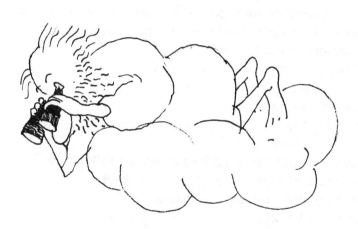

I have become convinced over these years
that I was right to be suspicious
of the whole kingship project.
They've all gone from bad to worse,
north and south alike.
Clearly what I need is not a king
to provide me with a human front,
but a prophet to provide me with a human voice.
Filled with my breath, my spirit,
he will proclaim loud and clear the word of the Lord.

My earliest attempts to provide
such spokesmen for God were clumsy enough,
as indeed they are in all the nations around.
No better than dancing dervishes.
But they're beginning to develop
into something more worthwhile
under my servant Elijah,
who's rightly pulled king Ahab down a peg or two.
I cringed, of course,
over the primitive demo he held on Mount Carmel,
and even more over the ferocious sequel.
Nor can I see his neurotic disciple Elisha
doing much better.
Young as he is, I notice he's already going thin on top.
But these are early days, and I must be patient.

What a bloody century!
Jezebel, Jehu, Athaliah and the rest!
I can see little relation
between what's been going on in Palestine
and the principles I had presumed were laid down
once for all at Mount Sinai.
People presume that what I inspired Moses to preach
were the Ten Suggestions.

Even the prophets on whom I'd pinned such hopes,
as new embodiments of Moses,
are at loggerheads with each other.
How can anyone tell
the genuine article from the fraud?
By the conviction with which he speaks?
The frauds are the most convinced,
not to mention convincing!

I was too pessimistic about the prophets.
Two have finally arrived
in whom I can again hear the voice of Moses.
They balance each other beautifully:
– Amos with his unrelenting denunciation
of market forces and social injustice
(the faces of the women in the congregation
when he addressed them as 'fat cows'!);
- Hosea with his gentler, yet more profound,
image of me as Lover.
Of course, it was only his disastrous marriage
that made him hit on such a bold metaphor.
But it highlights the fact that my marriage with Israel
hasn't been a bed of roses either.
Would a return to the desert
(and politically that's clearly in the offing)
give us both a chance of a second honeymoon?

We're definitely back on track.
Isaiah and Micah have not only
taken over where Amos and Hosea left off,
but have deepened their message.
Both are powerful preachers,
with first-class poetic honours going to Isaiah.
I find myself singing his *Vineyard Song*
over and over again.

Christened *YeshaYahu*, 'Salvation is from God',
he's naturally taken up the theme of Blind Faith.
For him, *the* sin is Adam's sin,
people imagining they can control their own destiny,
and forgetting they're in my hands.
Nice one, Isaiah.
But when it comes to the crunch,
I hope you also tell people that they *are* my hands.

Isaiah has now fastened on to the theme
of *Immanu El*, 'God is with us'.

How should one read this?
'God's with us, not against us'?
Or 'God's with us, not with anyone else'?

I'm worried that most people
will take it in the second sense,
and eventually even inscribe this blasphemy
on their army belts.

How can I stop this recurring idiotic assumption
that I am copyright material?

The irresistible advance
of the barbaric Assyrian empire
needed no prophets to foretell it.
Over these last weeks
it has finally engulfed the northern kingdom of Israel.
Droves and droves of my people
corralled into the concentration camp at Ramah,
and frogmarched off into exile.
Talk about Rachel weeping for her children!
Will we ever see them back?

The southern kingdom of Judah
is understandably keeping a low profile.
But to be on the safe side,
the king has commissioned a tunnel
to supply access to Jerusalem's water supply
in case of siege.

Isaiah is furious.

My jeremiad for Jeremiah.
A most sensitive soul,
he can see more clearly than most
that the fate of the northern kingdom
awaits Jerusalem too.
This means, of course,
that most of his message has to be threat,
when he'd far sooner be preaching promise.
Torn in two, and arousing more and more opposition
(they imprisoned him in a storage-well for a week),
he has taken to keeping a diary like me,
to record his private anguish.
It makes heartbreaking reading.

Yet, through all his pain,
this lonely man of sorrows
has come to a deeper understanding of me
than any of his contemporaries.
In his suffering he knows me
as he has never known me before.

He's convinced
that nobody's listened to a word he's said.
He's wrong.
My forecast is that the Jews will never again
be able to get Jeremiah out of their cistern.

Well, there it is!
For all the status
recently acquired by the Jerusalem Temple,
there being no other to rival it,
it's now gone as well.
Not a stone left upon a stone.
Today's Babylonian bonfire was a pitiable sight.

Yet I'm not grieving overmuch.
Perhaps people will now learn
that I'm present
where they never dream of looking for me
– in their hearts.

The Jewish exiles are not badly off.
They're well housed, well treated,
and even merrily setting up in business.
I did well to choose such a resourceful people.

They're lucky to have Ezekiel with them,
both as religious leader and as entertainer.
The visions that he retails are awe-inspiring,
and his pantomimes hilarious.
One of his sermons this month was both:
he asked the congregation to imagine
a field full of skeletons clanking back to life.
The laughter itself brought them back to life!
And what an awesome vision this gave them
of an Israel newly reborn in this Babylonian graveyard.

His preaching has encouraged
a small group of third-generation disciples
of the great Isaiah
to compose a number of poems
of consolation for the exiles.
These are so lovely
('Comfort ye, comfort ye, my people')
that they ought to be put to music.

So should the intensely moving poems
which depict the whole of this exiled people
as a Suffering Servant,
willing to undergo death
in order to bring knowledge of me to the pagan world.
I've made up my own tune to
'He was despised and rejected'.

Though I say it myself, it reduces me to tears.

How well this group of poets
have expressed what I've always hoped
Israel would become
– a channel of revelation to the whole world.
And how well they understand
that this can never be done by domination,
only by suffering.

I should know.

It's only a generation since the Jews were deported,
and already they're on their way back home.
Their liberator is the new master of the Middle East,
the Persian Cyrus.

People are saying the Messianic Age has come.
I suppose that in a way it has.
It now depends what people make of it.

The returned Jewish exiles
have certainly been enthusiastic.
Despite their experience
of my close presence among them, even in exile,
they've decided, now that they're back home,
that they again need a sacrament of my presence.

Today they consecrated
the newly rebuilt Jerusalem Temple.
It's nothing like as magnificent
(should I say ostentatious?) as Solomon's was.
In fact some of the older pensioners,
able to make comparisons,
broke into nostalgic tears.

But as their new psalms of praise
rose into the pine-laden evening air,
I felt that we now have the nucleus
of a true People of God.

A genius has appeared in India, full of my Spirit.
He illustrates perfectly
the fact that my word has always been heard
by all the nations of the earth,
and my light enlightened
everyone coming into my world.
But there are few who have become
as enlightened as my son Siddhartha Gautama.
I'm particularly intrigued by the fact
that his approach to me is so different
from the Jewish approach
that he seems at times to be saying the very opposite.
But he knows, as few do,
that in religious matters in particular,
there are many truths, not one.
To insist that I'm not to be thought of as an object,
whether of knowledge or of love,
he has taken to calling me The Void,
The Emptiness.
I like this.

I liked it still more
when his disciples recently expressed concern
that what he taught
was not to be found in the Holy Books.
'Then put it in', he said.
'But some of the things you say
contradict what the Books say.'
'Then change the Books.'
I could do with more people of such insight.
And with such a sense of the sacred.
And with such compassion for my world.

Editor's Note:
Western readers
(for whom this edition of excerpts is intended)
will have gathered that the Diary entries
here chosen for publication
have dealt almost exclusively with Israelites and Jews.
This italicised entry has been added,
among a few others,
to reassure them that God's interests
are not as exclusive as the Editor's,
and that further excerpts
about his relationship with other peoples
will appear in due course.

A century ago,
my hopes were for 'A True People of God'.
How naïve I sometimes am!
The Jews have reverted
to being as chauvinistic as ever.

Their present guru, Nehemiah,
has flouted planning permission regulations,
and boldly rebuilt the walls of Jerusalem.
It took him only a miraculous 52 days.
He claims he's done it for security reasons.
But with his narrow-minded emphasis
on observance of 'The Law',
he clearly wants the Jews to be separate,
hived off, different.
What is to become of them under such a regime?
Doesn't he realise there is no future in the past?

His people are complaining
that these days God seems to be a long way off.

So, who moved?

Ah now! Here's something different.
A series of delightful erotic poems
in which the hero is no longer the Great Law-giver
but the Great Lover.
'The Song of Songs'
they're calling it in the new spring lists.

I hope it *is* me it's all about!

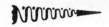

What a tornado
my Greek Alexander's turned out to be.
Within a short ten years,
he's unified the whole Middle East
under a single enlightened culture.

Will the Jews acclaim him as another Messiah,
as they did Cyrus?

What a hope!
They're withdrawing into their isolationist shells
with more determination than ever.

What a refreshing change, these days,
to see someone publishing a book that celebrates
my constitutional proneness to be merciful
rather than judgmental.

And what a hard-hitting critique it offers
of the narrow provincialism
that characterises most of the Israelite prophets.

Yes indeed, Jonah,
why shouldn't I be as concerned
for Nineveh as for Jerusalem?

If I was on a desert island,
this is one of the books I would want to take with me.

Two more magnificent pieces of Jewish writing
to restore my faith in this people.
One of them is a bold repudiation
of all the glib solutions
that superficial people keep offering
to the problem of suffering and evil.
Not that the author is able to offer
any alternative solution: he simply can't see any.
I find Job's honesty,
not to mention his blind trust in me,
singularly moving.

The preacher Ecclesiastes goes deeper still.
Even without any experience of evil,
even in the midst of peace and plenty,
he sees a world
that simply doesn't begin to satisfy
his infinite yearnings.
He doesn't pretend to have found any answers either,
but simply goes on and on questioning
the strange arrangements I've made for my world.
What faith here too,
to cling to me,
in spite of all those terrifying questions.

My poor Jewish people are under fire again.
A quite untypical successor of Alexander the Great
has taken over Palestine,
and is acting like a little Hitler.
All practice of the Jewish religion is to be proscribed,
and replaced by the Greek religion.

What madness!
I've nothing against the Greek religion,
but why not let people do their own particular thing?

Still, there's nothing like a bit of persecution
to put new life into a tired religion.
And I can't see the Jews
letting this tyrant get away with it.

Crisis always brings out the best in people,
and Judas Maccabaeus is from the top drawer.
His Resistance Movement
has gone from strength to strength.
The cost has been high, as in all revolutions,
but who (apart from bereaved families and me)
remembers this?

Today the Jerusalem Temple was rededicated.
Some wonderful new songs of praise.

A number of highly diverting stories have emerged
from the underground during these stirring months:
The Jewess (Judith),
in which the baddies are called 'Assyrians'
and get their comeuppance.
The Star (Esther), in which the 'Persians' get theirs.
God's In Charge (Daniel),
where the baddies are played by the 'Babylonians'.

Some distressingly racist stuff in these stories,
not to mention sheer brutality.
But then freedom fighters
can't live on a diet of Beatrix Potter.
Perhaps the tales are redeemed
by their preposterous implausibility.

And I *did* enjoy the story of Susanna!

The highly idealistic Maccabee Movement
is slowly degenerating
into a purely political struggle for power.

Is there any new movement,
however high-minded its origins,
that can escape this descent into hell?
Some Jews have protested with their feet,
and set up a hippy camp down by the Dead Sea.

Who knows?
They could be a voice crying in the wilderness
to prepare the way of the Lord.

Playing politics hasn't helped the Jews any.
They've simply become what they were
before the Exile,
pawns on the international chessboard.
This autumn
they've been incorporated into the Roman Empire.
I fear that for centuries hence
my story will now be told in Latin,
to the detriment of theology
and the dismay of countless generations
of school-children.

The Jews have finally got back
a semblance of independence,
thanks to the machinations of the Edomite Herod.
A sensuous, crafty and cruel man;
nobody would relish being his enemy,
or even one of his numerous wives.

Yet when I see what he's doing with his PCC
(Palestine Construction Company)
in the grandiose schemes
he has initiated throughout the country
– The Temple, Jericho, Masada, Caesarea, Samaria,
Herodium, Machaerus
– I get a sense of prodigality,
liberality and spendthrift magnificence
with which I can sympathise:
I'm like that too.

How skinflint, tight-fisted and parsimonious
most people are in comparison,
especially in what they call their religion.

I've warmed strongly to a new arrival in Galilee
– a builder named Jesus.
His name means 'Saviour'.
I can just see this man making the break-through
which could save the human race.

He's young yet, and has a lot to learn.
But he's beginning to show people
what it could mean to say
that human beings are destined to be
my 'sons and daughters',
filled with my godly Spirit as he is.
When he went down to the Jordan
to join John the Baptiser,
I said to myself, 'Yes, this *is* my son.'

I can see him becoming the spitting image of me,
so that people will want to call him *the* Son of God.
An apt title,
as long as people realise that what he became,
they can become too.

I'm reminded of Creation Day,
when I planned an Adam just like this.
My world has waited for this second Adam,
who allows me to be truly his 'father'.

What a genius these Asians have for storytelling!
The Europeans can't hold a candle to them,
in spite of already having ruled the civilised world
for longer than is good for them.
It's no wonder
that all my best spokesmen have been Asians.
They know
you can only teach good religion through good stories.

Jesus has already become an expert in the art.
He told some stories this week
which made even me burst out laughing.
The boy opening his newspaper
to find a snake among his chips!
The girl with the spoon poised over the egg-cup
only to find a scorpion climbing out!
The man who went looking for grapes on a cactus!
The woman offering
to remove a speck from her neighbour's eye,
without noticing the six-foot plank in her own!

We could do with a lot more theology of this kind.

It's a sheer joy to see Jesus
handling his thick-headed disciples
with such patience and tolerance.
Especially Peter, the thickest of the lot.

His attitude reflects
exactly the amazing grace
with which I've patiently tolerated
the human race over these millennia.
This man is like a window into me.
To see him is to see me, without distortion.

You could say that,
for all my mystery,
I am Jesus-shaped.
He is the whole truth about me,
being lived out in the life of an ordinary human being.

They're saying that Jesus can change water into wine.
What an inadequate metaphor
for someone who could change earth into heaven!

Jesus's preferential option for the poor
is beginning to arouse opposition.
Right from the outset,
he's identified himself with the disadvantaged,
the outcasts, the losers, the marginalised, the 'heretics'
– further evidence of how, day by day,
he becomes more and more like me.

His public teaching
– that it's people of this kind who are closest to me,
who here and now comprise
the 'Kingdom of God on Earth' –
this is naturally getting up the nose
of the religious powers that be.
They know that,
if this kind of theology catches on,
they'll be out of a job!

Meanwhile his preaching is taking Palestine by storm.

The opposition to Jesus has grown.
We're clearly close to flash point.

Tonight he brought his closest followers together
for the passover meal.
At the traditional breaking of the bread,
he spoke of his body soon to be broken in death.
And he repeated these forebodings
at the end of the meal,
when he spoke of his blood being poured out
as freely as the last cup of wine.

The police later picked him up.

My son, my son,
why do you think I have forsaken you?
Believe me, I'm closer to you than ever.
And you to me.

They killed him today, Friday.
A cruel and lingering death, but he went like a lamb.

I suppose it was inevitable.
Given what my world has become
over these thousands of years,
it was bound to be at cross purposes
with those who share my priorities,
and show themselves to be true children of mine.

Do I regard it as a tragedy?
How could I regard it as anything else?
If sparrows don't fall to the ground
without it tearing my heart out,
what should I say
about the death of this son of mine?

Yet I refuse to think of it as an unmitigated disaster.
This won't be the end of the Jesus story.
He has not died into nothing.
He has died into me.

Jesus's friends are already experiencing him
as being closer to them now
than he ever was in his lifetime.
His women friends in particular.
Killing him has made him live.

So that when people ask them where Jesus is now,
they no longer point to the cemetery
as they were doing last Friday.
They point to their own community,
in which Jesus is marvellously embodied
in a new way.

It's as if his death has allowed the godly Spirit
with which he was filled
to pour out into the wide world.

Those who live in that Spirit
are already in my presence,
as Jesus always was,
and still is.

Not two months after he died,
Jesus's followers had already grown
to three thousand.
This week they number five thousand.

This could be the beginning of something big.

4801, 4802, 4803,
4804, 4,805,
4,806,
4,807 ...

The real expansion of 'Christianity'
(as it is now beginning to be called)
began with Paul.

A human dynamo,
only five feet high but with a reach beyond the stars,
he was the first to realise
that Jesus's vision
could not be contained within the shell
of traditional Judaism.
It needed to explode
into the whole Mediterranean world.
And that's where Paul has been,
like a fireball,
over these last six years,
setting up Christian communities in every major city,
even in red-light Corinth.

Orthodox Judaism is standing aghast,
and relations with the *Yiddisher Mamma*
have been strained to breaking point.

But it needn't come to formal schism, need it?

It's happened.
Christianity's foray into the west
has turned it into something very different
from what Jesus had in mind.

This doesn't mean it shouldn't have happened:
it was inevitable.
But it does mean
that it's become more and more alien to Judaism.

Today was probably the last straw.
Jerusalem's been smashed to pieces
by the Roman army,
and the shattered Jews
have withdrawn even further into their shell.

The allegiance of Christianity to Jerusalem is broken.
It's going its own way.

Some friends of Jesus
– Matthew, Mark, Luke and John –
have published their interpretations
of what Jesus meant to them,
and of what, in retrospect,
he continues to mean to them.

I have not been able to find out
the order in which they wrote,
but I'm glad that the four are so different
that people can compare these writings
and contrast them.

I hope no one will be so stupid
as to imagine that they are simple pieces of reportage.
They are far more profound than that.

New Year reflections.

Distinct as Christians now are from Jews,
they haven't been spared over these centuries
from the persecution
that used to fall only on Jewish heads.

Stephen, Peter, Paul, Ignatius, Polycarp, Irenaeus,
Origen, Cyprian, Felicity, Perpetua, Agatha
– what a roll call of heroes and heroines
to rival the Jewish saints.

And what a grim commentary
on the grim reality my world has turned into.

Christian-bashing,
popular for the last 300 years, has stopped.
The shock seems to have addled Christian brains.

They first stood agape
when Christianity was declared
the official religion of the Roman Empire.
But then they actually welcomed it!
After all,
it now allows them to bash everyone else
as hard as they like,
with the cross on which
the Roman Empire crucified Jesus!

Christianity's been hijacked.
It's become the religion of the powerful.
Can it ever recover from this shameful compromise?
I don't know whether to laugh or cry
over the irony of it.
No wonder thousands are rushing off
to live in the desert,
to dissociate themselves from such a farce.

But that's hardly a solution either.

I see that Constantine's shrewdly saved up
his Christian baptism till his deathbed.

He presumably wanted to make sure
his sins were not remitted
till he'd got them all committed.

Now that the Christian Church is headed
by a divinised and unapproachable Emperor,
it was inevitable that Jesus should begin
to be robed in the same inhuman garb.

Thank goodness
that many Christians have risen up in angry protest.
And my blessings on the saintly priest Arius who,
in the name of common humanity and common sense,
has made this protest vocal.

But I fear that his protest will be smothered,
and that for centuries to come
Christianity will be saddled
with a lopsided and inhuman Jesus,
whom nobody will be able to recognise as a brother.

As I thought.
After a century of quibbling,
the Christians have officially concluded
that Jesus must have had two natures,
one divine and one human.

Nobody seems surprised by the announcement:
for most Christians
Jesus is no longer part of the human race.

You'd have to say he had two heads
before anyone would raise an eyebrow
over such an odd theology.

I'm glad to see
that some of my Egyptian Christians
have refused to countenance
such misleading language.
Why will people keep on trying
to unscrew the inscrutable?

Today marks the death of Simon,
a Christian hermit who for the last twenty years
has marooned himself
on top of a sixty-seven-foot pillar.

He was a kind of parable of the present state of play:
most of my Christians are up the pole.

Welcome home to sanity, Lofty!

A welcome break in the weary scene.
Another Paul has arisen in northern Europe.
His name is Patrick.
A Roman like Paul,
and filled with the same selfless zeal,
he's preached the Gospel to the Irish so effectively that,
almost to a man
(perhaps I should say almost to a woman),
they've become followers of Jesus.

I was bemused by his attempt
to elucidate the mystery that I am
in terms of a shamrock leaf.
But then the Buddha did much the same thing
with a lotus flower.

What is incontestable is
that he's planted in Ireland
an understanding of the Gospel
such as I doubt can ever be uprooted.

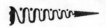

The wild Angles,
still exhausted after their recent invasion
and occupation of Britain,
have now themselves been invaded.

A group of monks has arrived from Rome,
and persuaded the king to become a Christian.

Less couth than their Irish neighbours,
perhaps even these Angles
might be transformed into angels
under the influence of my son Jesus.

More good news.

*A much needed religious renewal in the Middle East, long
submerged in a welter of cheerless superstition.
My eternal word has again been given flesh,
this time in the life and teaching of Muhammad.*

*Within a few years he's changed
the face of the Arab world,
and established* Islam *(submission)
to the one and only Me
as the only worthwhile basis of living.*

*I've no doubt that his movement
will degenerate into triumphalism,
power politics and extremism;
which religious movement hasn't?*

*But what Muhammad has preached
is brotherhood and compassion,
because he has always known me
as the All Merciful One.*

See Editor's Note on p. 45

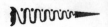
As I feared,
the followers of Moses, Buddha,
Jesus and Muhammad
are all now merrily persecuting each other.

I suspect that religion is only good for good people;
the bad it only makes worse.
Most people have just enough religion
to make them hate,
and not enough to make them love.

What is obvious is
that if people keep taking an eye for an eye,
the whole world will soon be blind.

The Frankish king Charlemagne
has nostalgically revived
the long defunct Roman Empire,
and proclaimed himself Holy Roman Emperor.

So the farce continues.
Can no one but me see
the irony of sanctifying an Empire which,
even if it hadn't tried to liquidate Jesus,
would still be
the very antithesis of all that he stood for?

Meanwhile barbaric Vikings from Scandinavia
are massacring my beloved Christians in Angle-land.

Well, these at least know
that they haven't been called
to dominate others by force.

The Greek bishop Photios
has protested against the overweening claims
of the Romans to rule the Christian roost.

Their reply has been to excommunicate him.

I suspect we've not heard the last of this
east-west tension.

One expects the occasional blasphemy from a bishop,
but not on the scale we heard this week.

The bishop of Rome has until now
been accorded the courtesy title
'Vicar of (or Stand-In for) Peter',
who died in Rome.
Today he upgraded the title to 'Vicar of Christ'.

His first act was to excommunicate
the Holy Roman Emperor,
just to make sure everyone knows who is Caesar.

Whatever next?
Will he now go on to claim he's God Almighty?

No wonder the eastern Christians,
long offended by these Roman antics,
have regretfully separated themselves from the west.

It is, in a way, a disaster for the followers of Jesus,
whose dying prayer for them
was that they would always be at one.
But given the unwieldy monolith
that Christianity has become,
it's perhaps no bad thing that, for the time being,
it becomes a little more pluralistic.

Time for healing the wounds later.

Meanwhile I'm delighted that the Russian people,
having sent out ambassadors to discover

a religion that would be worthwhile adopting,
were so overwhelmed
by the splendour of the eastern liturgy
that they've all agreed to become followers of Jesus.

I expect great things from my Russian Christians.

For the last hundred years
the Christian west has been conducting a crusade
to restore Palestine to Christian hands.

A rather wasteful operation,
since my Muslim people
have venerated the memory of Jesus
in the holy places
with the utmost decorum.

And how comic for Frenchmen
to crown themselves as Kings of Jerusalem.
Because that's where Jesus was crowned?

What's revolted me most
is the way this rabble of an army
has used the name of Jesus
to legitimise their struggle for power,
prestige and loot.
They've turned not only against Muslims,
but against the Jews as well,
and eventually even
against their fellow Christians of the east.
Today they sacked Christian Constantinople,
and left it in ruins.

Western Christianity will stink
in the nostrils of the east
for centuries to come.

Francis and Dominic
– what a beatific pair
to bring a ray of hope into these dark ages!

Francis,
with his Buddha-like
veneration and compassion
for the least of my creatures.

And Dominic,
with his faith in the goodness of creation,
and his almost Islamic zeal to spread this good news
through the pervading gloom.

Why do I keep enthusing
over the acute vision of my prophets,
when it so soon turns to myopia?

The descendants of the saintly Dominic
are already deeply involved in the 'Holy' Inquisition,
gaily amputating 'diseased limbs',
as they put it,
in order to safeguard the health of the 'body'.

But killing people doesn't defend the truth:
it simply kills people.

Why do these fanatics never think of judging people
by their behaviour, instead of by their creed?
Here's me constantly on the look out
for spiritual fruits,
and all I keep getting is religious nuts.

Meanwhile a Solemn Council has decreed
that Jews are to wear distinctive clothing,
and to be segregated into ghettos.

My poor people, the apple of my eye!

How does it come about
that religious people
can practise such abominable cruelty, barbarity,
intolerance and insensitivity,
and in between times
build such breathtakingly beautiful cathedrals,
decorate them with such exquisite sculptures,

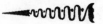 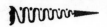
painting and glass,
and fill them with such heavenly music?

I'm delighted that people enter these buildings
to find peace and beauty,
joy and a sense of my presence.
But I'd far sooner they experienced these realities
in their daily living:
don't they realise I'm present there too?

One pope apparently being thought insufficient,
my western Christians have opted for two.
Not surprisingly, they've excommunicated each other.

Since both are infallible,
I wonder where we go from here.

Well secluded from such childishness,
a wise and saintly recluse in Northwic
has published her visions of hell,
expressing her amazement
at not seeing any Jews there,
in spite of countless anathemas.

She'll no doubt be accused of heresy.
But I say, good on her.

And also on my Sienese Catherine.
And on all women
who have the courage to tell the theologians
what nonsense they frequently talk.

The success of the religious orders
founded by my sons Benedict, Francis,
Dominic and others,
has generated enormous wealth.
Not to mention smugness, pomposity and avarice.

It's difficult to find any vestige of the Gospel
in these bowdlerisations of Christianity,
where the liturgy has become a clerical preserve,
where Masses are multiplied
and can be bought for money,
and where even the 'merits of Jesus and the Saints'
are up for sale.
And all with the blessing
of those 'shepherds of the flock',
the bishops.
The crosses they are putting in front of their names
ought to be noughts.

There have been protests, of course,
not least in the preaching of the holy Czech priest,
John Hus.

They burnt him today.

I wept to see an old woman
faithfully bringing her faggot to add to the fire.
What they've done to her
is infinitely worse
than what they've done to John.

Europe has at last discovered
my gentle and devout people in the Americas.

I fear for them.
They'd have warmed to the teaching of Jesus,
but I'm not sure how far they will benefit
from European 'Christianity'.

In any case,
I imagine things over there will change somewhat.

John Hus is a hundred years in his grave,
but his voice still speaks
in the preaching of an Augustinian monk,
my son Martin Luther.

Four years ago he boldly published
the ninety-five 'theses'
which he was prepared to defend in public debate.
Like all protestants, he went too far.

But there's no denying that the corruptions he listed
– in the liturgy, in the exercise of authority,
in the freedom of conscience,
and above all in the concept of how people relate to me
– all cry out loud for reform.
'Here I stand', he nobly cried out like Jesus,
'I can no other.'
They excommunicated him last month.

This month he finds himself
at the head of a considerable alternative Church.
It's the last thing he wanted,
and he's insisting that his bewildered followers
shouldn't call themselves 'Lutherans',
but simply 'Christians'.

Meanwhile the pope has issued an encyclical letter
with the opening words,
'Obedience, the highest of all the virtues.'
Above honesty? Integrity? Sense of responsibility?

Locking the stable door even more firmly?

Not before time,
the official Roman Church has begun its own reform.

A Council has been called at Trent,
but all it has managed so far
is a depressing series of anathemas
against the Reformers:
sixty-three over the last two months.

My servant Erasmus has forecast
that the breach between Rome and the Protestants
is now irreparable.
What pessimism!

Yet it's obvious
this wound will take a good half-century to heal.

What an unconscionable time it's taken Europeans
to discover two of my prize creations,
the potato and the tobacco leaf.

I had meant them to be a big surprise
for anyone coming to the Americas for the first time.

Walter Raleigh is ecstatic,
as if he'd had an extra birthday.

Great confusion among my English Christians.
They're unsure
whether they belong to Rome or to the Reformers.

Queen Elizabeth has solved the problem
by decreeing that they belong to both.
A perplexed 'Church of England'
has therefore been born,
willing to accept any changes
as long as they make no difference.

I see they're already arguing
about whether or not they should wear vestments
for the liturgy.
They've clearly caught religion!

They're also beginning to prove
what strong faith they have
by massacring each other.

Catholics can now
be easily distinguished from Protestants.
The former burn their rivals, the latter behead them.

Maybe there would be more Christians in the world
if it weren't for the Christians.

One can sympathise with anyone's desire
to blow up the Houses of Parliament.
Guy Fawkes has upset the English
by actually trying to do it.

It's the fireworks for him, I'm afraid.

A charismatic Church of England minister,
with king David's own genius for composing psalms
(they even rhyme!),
has reluctantly gone out on a limb.
They've named his followers after him
– Wesleyan Methodists.

Obviously any breach in Christian unity
is to be deplored.
On the other hand,
if the only unity people know
is a Kremlin-like uniformity,
they ought not to be surprised
if some hive off to do their own thing.
After all, when I said, 'Let there be flowers',
I didn't mean only roses.

Nothing like a bit of variety.

I expect great things from my Methodist people.
Especially since they've shown
such sensitivity over ministry.
Ministers were meant to be servants of the community,
not its task-masters.
The Church, the Gospel, the Sacraments
– these are not the preserve of a male clerical caste.
They belong to the whole of my people.
Ministers are there simply for the sake of order.

The Methodists understand this.
At the moment.

Today's earthquake,
which pretty well wiped Lisbon off the map
and left over fifty thousand dead,
has shaken believers the world over.

The more sadistically minded are interpreting it
as my retribution on a wicked world.
I wish such people
would stop calling themselves believers.
They don't know the first thing about me.

The more thoughtful are asking
how I could allow such a thing.
Why didn't I prevent it?
But, omnipotent as I am,
'allowing' and 'preventing' is not within my power.
I have created a vulnerable world
where fire not only warms people but also burns them,
where water not only slakes their thirst
but also drowns them.
Who but plastic robots could live in a world
that was otherwise?
Given the world as it is, what's the use of a prayer
that two plus two don't make four?
Or should I turn iron girders into rubber
if they fall on people's heads?

What people need to understand is
that in disasters of this kind, I am not absent,
but more present than ever.
I am not the God whom philosophers and theologians
call *impassibilis* (impassive?) or *apathetos* (apathetic?).

I am the God seen in Jesus,
more present (and heart-broken) in his tragic death
even than in his radiant life.
And more anxious than ever in 'bad times'
than in 'good times'
that people reveal my presence
in the love they show for each other.

'How can anyone find God in this situation?'
people say.
How can anyone help fish find the ocean?

Revolution is in the air.

First that of the North American colonists,
who successfully declared their independence
from their British nanny two decades ago.

And now that of the French,
who have overthrown the corrupt system
under which they've long lived,
and set up a republic.
An indescribably ugly Reign of Terror is in process,
to make it clear that human rights are not for everyone.
But when you screw down the lid
on overheated kettles, they eventually explode.

Certainly the French Revolution will ensure
that liberty, equality and neighbourly love
remain permanently written into the world's agenda.
Pity that the movement had such minimal support
from the Christian churches.

As if to compensate for this loss of prestige,
in the New World as well as in the Old,
western Christianity has begun
to look for new fields to conquer
in Africa.
Missionaries are going there in droves,
aware of the millions of ears
that haven't heard the good news of Jesus.
My blessing goes with them,
though I'm not too sure that baptism by hosepipe
is the answer to Africa's needs.

Especially since it has meant
the virtual destruction of the religion
by which Africans have, for centuries, served me,
and the impositon of a culture
quite alien to their ancestral traditions.

What will become of Christian Africa
remains to be seen.
For the moment,
the land which the Africans had,
and the bible which the white man had,
simply seem to have changed hands.

I was relieved to see
that the idiotic papal ban on the Jesuits
has finally been withdrawn.
They've much to contribute.

If a Dominican, Franciscan and Jesuit
were praying together and the lights failed,
I imagine that the Dominican
would deliver a philosophical lecture
on the properties of light,
the Franciscan would compose a poem
about Brother Darkness and Sister Light,
and the Jesuit would get up and mend the fuse.

My world needs people of all three kinds.

As I look back over the century just ended,
which had aspects as depressing as any other,
I take consolation from
the Three Wise Men it produced
– Charles, Karl and Sigmund.

All three, Darwin, Marx and Freud,
revelling (as I did) in the glorious 'Enlightenment'
which had burst upon the world in the 1700's,
insisted on discovering the meaning of life
not by reading holy books but by studying people
– biologically, historically, socially and psychologically.

They've dug deeper into the human psyche
than any of their predecessors,
brilliant as these had been,
especially the British philosophers.
They've revolutionised
the world's understanding of itself.

Theologians will now need to revolutionise theirs,
I'm glad to say.
As a wit recently remarked,
since I am, by definition,
the ultimate and unknowable mystery,
theology (or the study of Me) is the only *ology*
whose practitioners don't know
what they're talking about.

Of course, the new 'enlightened' thinkers
tend to be rather cocky
about what human reason can achieve.

But I find their sense of confidence in the human race
preferable to the inhuman gloom
of those who have for centuries claimed
to be my official representatives.
Their lopsided understanding of the word 'God'
would drive even me to atheism.

I lament over the Roman decree *Lamentabili*.
It has labelled all these marvellous new insights
as 'Modernism' and condemned the lot,
as if the only wisdom lay in the past.
Acorns, the pope seems to say,
are meant to grow into giant acorns, not trees.

Until now, people have acclaimed him as a wit.
They're half right.

Pressure has even been put on my loyal servants
in the Jerusalem *Ecole Biblique*
to switch their studies
from the 'dangerous' Old Testament to the New.

Don't people realise that the new learning
is going to give them even bigger headaches there?

It had to happen.
The bitter sectarianism,
in which the various Christian denominations
have been locked for centuries, is ending.

A worldwide group of Protestant missionaries
met in Edinburgh today, and agreed
that the crazy feud has been not only wasteful
but counter-productive.
They have decided that from now on
they will cooperate, not compete.

My blessing on this faith-filled gesture.
I can see these generous people going even further,
and finding the need to form
something like a World Council of Churches,
a forum in which the Churches
will finally listen to each other.

But I imagine it will take my Roman Christians
some years to join such a worthwhile dialogue.

After four years of blood-letting,
one would have thought
Europe would finally settle down.
But lidded kettles continue to blow their tops.

This year has seen democracy ousting
Emperors in Holy Russia,
English overlords in God's own Ireland,
and kings in Eternal Rome.

Slowly, slowly, it seems,
some of my ideas catch on.

A great day for Christianity.

In a *concordat* signed this month,
Mussolini has allowed the Vatican
to fly its own flag
and issue its own stamps.

Big deal.

The democratising movement of the twenties
hasn't served my beloved German people well.

They've had foisted on them, as leader or führer,
a psychopathic ex-theological student
who threatens to out-Nero Nero.
I first thought of him as a laughable disaster.
I no longer think he's laughable.

Already he's declared an explicitly racist war
against my Jewish people,
and is gaining a surprising amount of support
from the Churches.

What sort of anti-semitism
lies hidden in the pages of the Gospels
that subconsciously authorises so-called Christians
to sanction such an atrocity?

The sons of the first World War's victims
have been cynically drafted
to provide a replay of the farce.
Is World War II
any more likely to solve the world's problems
than the first?

For the moment, almost unnoticed,
the European Jews are bearing the brunt of it.
Four million of them
have already been herded into concentration camps,
systematically dehumanised, and finally gassed.
No doubt more will follow.

An outraged rabbinical court
sat in judgment on me for three days this week
before they came to a verdict.
They found me guilty.
Then they prayed.
My hands are tied.

But not my eyes.
They are like rivers.

They finished off the war today
by exploding an 'atom' bomb over Japan.
It incinerated thousands in an instant,
and crippled tens of thousands more.

It's been called the ultimate in horror.

It isn't.
My human race is capable of much worse than this.

The world hasn't seen many saintly popes.
A double welcome therefore for 'Good Pope John'.

Down to earth, human through and through,
and with an engaging simplicity,
he's beginning to restore
my punch-drunk Roman Church to sanity.

He threatens to open windows
that have been shut tight for centuries.
Woe betide those susceptible to draughts.

What I've most welcomed is
his official proclamation
that the current interfaith dialogue
is the work of the holy Spirit.
Until now it's been labelled the work of the devil.

The Vatican theologians are working hard
to explain this volte-face
as a 'Development of Doctrine'.

Why has it taken Christians so long
to realise what John has seen in a flash?
That they don't need to discover a new unity,
but an older one.
That what unites people is infinitely more important
than what divides them.
That people already are one;
they only imagine they're not.
That the fundamental principle
on which I've based my world

is not that one is half of two,
but that two are halves of one.

John knows this.

With his humble honesty,
he's the sort of person
who might re-convene the Vatican Council
to conclude
its deeply unsatisfactory unfinished business.

Now that really would be something.

All the bishops who attended Vatican II
speak of it as an education.
Like all education, it has been a gradual growth
from cocksure ignorance to thoughtful uncertainty.
It'll take a long time for the monolithic Roman Church
to get used to such pluralism within.

The current jingle perhaps sums it up:
Vatican One, for good or ill,
Declared the pope infallible.
Vatican Two, the recent sequel,
Made pope and bishops more co-equal.
And that is why, twixt you and me,
The pope's not calling Vatican Three.

For all his loyalty to John's Council,
the new pope has taken that 1965 jingle to heart.

With most of his advisers telling him that
the traditional Roman argument against contraception
no longer holds water,
he decided this summer to play solo.
His encyclical *Humanae Vitae*
simply reinforced the traditional Roman teaching.

There have been protests galore,
not least from the priests who (unlike him)
have to deal with the problem at pastoral level.
The only response the poor man has been able to make
is to repeat, 'But I'm infallible.'

Unfortunately, everyone knows what it means
when you're reduced to banging the table.

Roman Catholics are having to re-think
the role of the pope in the Church.

Not before time.

My hopes rise for my beloved English people.
What wisdom they've shown
in choosing a Prime Minister
who so appreciates Francis of Assisi
and the Parable of the Good Samaritan
that she quoted both of them in her opening speech.

Her people have already taken to calling her
'The Blessed Margaret'.

Perhaps we shall finally see a decade
which will transform England
into a genuinely caring and compassionate society.

For the last five years
Rome has had a Polish pope.

Out of a natural patriotism,
he's been making some pretty bold political statements
about the wretched situation in his homeland.
I am with him all the way.
In my book, such political action
is a far more profound act of religion than any liturgy.

Why then does he take such a negative attitude
towards the theologians
who are making the same sort of political protest
in the even more desperate Third World?
He's obviously disturbed
by the violent undertones
in some of their strident demands for justice.

But there are times
when violence is the only way
of ensuring a hearing for moderation.

Certainly the Christian communities
that are forming around such protest movements
are a more faithful witness to the Gospel
than what currently passes for Christianity.
They're the hope of the coming centuries.

I don't need a Church
which only comforts the afflicted.
I need a Church which afflicts the comfortable.

All action for the liberation of the oppressed
has my blessing.
Especially action for the liberation of women,
who have been silently oppressed
throughout history.
Since they comprise a good half of the human race,
I find it distinctly odd
that they've been allowed almost no say
in the way things should be run.

Not least in the Church.

My Anglican people have done well
to choose a professor of theology
as the new bishop of Durham.

He's already stunned people
by inviting them to look seriously
at the implications of taking the stories
of the Virgin Birth and of the Empty Tomb
literally.

The press purports to be scandalised,
as if it cared a hoot
about the meaning of these exquisite pieces of poetry.

I have to admit that,
in a puckish desire to keep the controversy going,
I departed from my customary manner of acting
and zapped York Minster!

Up here,
we laughed over the affair unto the ages of ages.

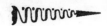

I'm afraid I'm beginning to find ARCIC almost farcic.

The
'Anglican-Roman Catholic International Commission',
as it calls itself,
has been sitting for years
to try to resolve the minimal differences
that divide the two Churches.

To their own surprise (but to no one else's)
they arrived at the conclusion that
there is now no reason
why they should not mutually recognise each other
as members of the same family.

Taking fright,
the powers that be have laboured
to find yet further unresolved differences,
and given birth to ARCIC II.

Where will it all end?
ARCIC IC?

My servant, Mikhail Gorbachev,
avid for peace
in a world that has seen too many pointless wars,
has proposed that both east and west
should begin disarming themselves
of the astronomically costly weapons
piled up on both sides.

They're already so numerous,
he's pointed out,
that they could destroy six planets.
And we only have the one.

A not unreasonable proposal,
one would have thought.
If it was in my gift,
I would award this man the Nobel Peace Prize.

The western leaders remain sceptical,
unable to believe that an atheist
might understand the Gospel
better than they do.

The Iranian Ayatollah Khomeini died today.

Welcome home,
my anachronistic son,
and meet the other mediaeval popes.

There were forces
burrowing away at the Berlin Wall
long before it was dismantled.
But its removal today
has been a potent and dramatic symbol.

All sorts of walls,
particularly psychological ones,
will now tumble.

The forty years divorce
between eastern and western Europeans
has dehumanised both.
Not to say impoverished them:
the east is bankrupt.
The economic implications of a reunion
are so complex that even I can't understand them.

For the moment,
like a newly reconciled couple,
the two need to get to know each other
all over again.

It'll take time.

I feel a kind of nostalgic sadness
over the collapse of Communism in Europe.

Its philosophy of
'From each according to his capacity,
to each according to his need'
had a sort of Gospel ring about it.
No one has had the courage
to put such a philosophy into practice on a large scale,
least of all the so-called Christian countries.

Of course, it was naïve to imagine
that everyone would be fired by such a high ideal,
or that imposing it willy-nilly on all
would automatically make them warm to it.
Human nature is far more geared
to a philosophy of
'From each according to his rapacity,
to each according to his greed.'

My fear is that,
newly aware of the power of market forces,
and newly distrustful of anything
that doesn't make money,
my gentle easterners will simply become
as greedy as my hardnosed westerners.

But for the moment the ending of the Cold War
has brought some sort of stability to the world.
No doubt there are surprises round the corner
to stop us all getting too complacent.

As the year 2000 approaches,
the number of apocalyptic alarmists
is beginning to swell, as it has done
at the end of each millennium in the past.

'The End is upon us', they excitedly announce.
They're right, of course, in one sense.
The ultimates are always today rather than tomorrow.

But chronologically such panic is laughable,
since we're still in the days of the early Church.
I have plans light-years ahead for my human race.

This diary has hardly begun!

Editor's Note:

The 1991 Diary of God,
being in current use,
has not yet been made available for researchers.

End Note:

I note that my servant Hubert Richards
has been trying to reconstruct my private diary.
A noble effort.

Miles off the mark, of course,
since his understanding of me is severely limited.

But whose isn't?